CU...IES
BEEKEEPING

L. R. Croft

Northern Bee Books
1990

First published by Elmwood Books 1989.
Second edition 1990, Northern Bee Books
Scout Bottom Farm, Scout Bottom Road,
Mytholmroyd, Hebden Bridge, W. Yorks. HX7 5JS

British Library Cataloguing in Publication Data
Croft, L. R.
Curiosities of Beekeeping.
1. Bee-keeping
I. Title
638'. 1

ISBN 0 907908 52 7

Printed by Arc & Throstle Press, Todmorden, Lancs.

CONTENTS

THE GLOBE BEE-VEIL.

PREFACE

No one species of animal has inspired so many people in so many different ways as has the bee. For almost 5000 years man has tried to domesticate this insect with varying degrees of success. During this long period he has come to treat this small creature with considerable respect, so much so, that today the bee is often used to represent integrity, purity, industry and a host of other virtues.

It has recently been stated that no other single insect has had so much written about it as the honey bee. Even today many excellent books on beekeeping appear almost daily from the publishers, so much so, it would seem almost superfluous to add to that number. Indeed the U.S. Bureau of Entomology has a working catalogue of 20,000 titles on this one insect. In the light of this fact one is forced to ask — what more can be written? Indeed this should surely turn any sensible person away from trying to add to this voluminous library. Nevertheless the fact that so much has been written is probably some justification for what I have now compiled, for this consists of a collection of occasional notes, obtained from, in the main, obscure sources. Therefore at the outset I make no apology that what follows is something of a miscellany. Indeed it is.

With the material obtained I have attempted to paint a series of pictures on various aspects of beekeeping, which to my mind awaken interest. I therefore hope that they will entertain and occupy a pleasant perusal from time to time. John Ruskin once described what he would like to find in a book about bees, he wrote:

> I don't in the least want a book to tell me how many species of bee there are; nor what grounds there may be for suspecting that one species is another species etc. Neither do I want a book to tell what a bee's inside is like, nor whether it has brains in the small of its back,......
> But I want a book to tell, for instance, how a bee buzzes etc.,

I have now attempted to compile such a book and I hope my readers will not feel I have fallen too short of this aim.

L. R. Croft.

1.

BEEKEEPING OLD AND NEW

THE ORIGIN AND BELIEF IN TANGING

"Tanging" refers to the racket created by banging a bunch of keys, or other metal object, against a warming-pan, or kettle. This was a fairly widespread practice carried out by cottagers in the belief that it caused a swarm to settle. It is a practice of considerable historical interest for we know that Virgil was familiar with it. In his fourth *Georgics* he wrote:

> When you see the host
> Floated skyward through the limpid summer air,
> A cloud of darkness borne upon the wind,
> Be sure of this: they seek a pleasant stream,
> A leafy dwelling place. Here you must spread
> Bruised sprigs of balm and humble honey-wort,
> And jangle cymbals of Great Cybele.

Charles Butler in his *Feminine Monarchie* (1609, Edition) maintained that it had two merits. These were; firstly, it signified to other beekeepers that a swarm was in the air and that its rightful owner was following it. And secondly, it served to drown the so-called "piping" of the queen, thereby inducing the bees to pitch nearby. Tusser Redivivus in 1744 wrote:

> The tinkling after them with a warming pan, frying pan,
> kettle, is of good use to let the neighbours know you have
> a swarm in the air, which you claim wherever it lights,
> but I believe of very little purpose to the reclaiming of
> the bees, who are thought to delight in no noise but their
> own.

I discovered a delightful explanation for this custom published in the correspondence column of the *Daily Mail,* in 1911, under the heading: "A Woman the Bees Love," it read:

Dear Sir,

Your correspondent in his pleasant Summer Diary asks whether he is right in supposing that the beating of tin cans can make bees swarm.

I am an old countrywoman, my knowledge of bees goes back nearly 60 years and as I have always had a positive affection for them I would like to answer his question.

The rough music made by a warming-pan and door key is generally what they use in country cottage gardens, not to make bees swarm but to drown the voice of their young queen and leader, so that they will have to settle near instead of flying away for miles, as they will sometimes when it is quiet.

When a young swarm is ready to leave the parent hive, if you listen at the back of the hive after dusk you will hear a single bee, presumably the young queen, make a clear and distinct trumpeting noise at intervals of a few seconds. They are sure when that is the case, to swarm the next morning, and I believe the queen keeps up that sound until the swarm finds a suitable resting place: hence the racket to prevent her orders being heard.

Signed: Betsy Powner

Rosebank Cottage, Broseley.

TANGING

On the other hand a writer to the BBJ of November 1891 commented:

> According to local custom if a man's bees swarmed on
> or into his neighbour's garden, or field, he had the right
> to follow his swarm withersoever they went provided he
> ranged them with key and shovel and could keep them
> in view.

It seems likely, however, that the origin of this custom had another purpose, namely to attract the attention of the beekeeper himself. In all likelihood the cottager, at swarming time, would be away in the fields, so he would have to put his wife and children on the alert looking out for swarms. When a swarm issued they would immediately clang together any suitable metal objects so as to attract his attention and get him back to the cottage as quickly as possible, so as to help retrieve the swarm.

BEE-HUNTING

One early method of bee hunting required the following provisions:- wax, vermilion, honey, and a small pocket compass. The bee hunter so equipped would select a flat stone on which some wax would be burned. Then he would drop honey around on which he sprinkled vermilion. He would then retire to wait for the bees to appear. Usually they would be attracted by the smell of the wax and finding the honey would become tinged with the vermilion. Next, fixing his compass he would determine the direction of flight of the bees, as invariably they adopted a straight flight on returning home. The timing of the bee's return was recorded, the bee being recognised by the vermilion marking. Thus knowing the direction and distance he could make a resonable guess as to where the nest was situated.

A similar approach was adopted by the Australian aborigines. They would wait at a waterhole for bees to come to collect water. They would then use a special weed that exudes a sticky gum to flick a piece of feather fluff on to the back of the bee. The bee so weighted down could easily be followed through the forest. As the native followed he would mark the trees and when the nest was located the wild honey was gathered.

FLOATING APIARIES

In ancient Egypt the practice of transporting beehives by barge was followed. The hives were collected from different villages along the banks and arranged in pyramidal piles on the barges, which were floated down the river. During the journey the boats would be halted for various periods according to the local flora. In all the journey took about three months and the delicious honey collected included jasmine and orange blossom. The custom continued into modern times for the celebrated traveller Karsten Niebuhr (1733-1815) once recorded how he saw on the Nile between Cairo and Damietta, a convoy of 4000 hives in transit between Upper Egypt to the coast.

A similar custom existed in France where beehives were often transported afloat on rivers and canals. One bee barge was constructed with capacity enough for one hundred hives. By floating up and down the river the bees were free to gather honey from the flowers along the banks.

The journal *Nature* of 26th September, 1895, described a floating beekeeping exhibition in Moscow. A barge measuring 70 metres in length and 8 metres broad, was fitted up with a museum and a garden with trees and flower beds. Hives of all kinds, both old and new, accommodated with bees were installed. The museum also contained examples of beekeeping appliances and products. The staff in charge of the exhibition consisted of both beekeepers and entomologists. The barge was towed down the river out of Moscow by twenty horses, ten on each bank. In all six towns and twenty villages were visitied. Travelling was done only during the night; during the daylight hours a halt was made. The exhibition proved a great success. The idea and finance for it was provided by Herr F. Motschalkin an enthusiastic beekeeper.

THE SULPHURING OF BEES

During ancient Greek and Roman times beekeeping was conducted so that the surplus honey from the hives could be harvested without killing the bees. During later times this practice was discontinued and honey would be collected only after the slaughter of the colony of bees. With skep beekeeping this was carried out in the autumn when the beekeeper decided which hives would be kept and which destroyed. A general rule was to take all the hives that were full of honey. Of the lighter ones only those three years old and older were taken. A pit would be dug in the ground and towards evening sulphur burned in it. The skep was placed over the pit and the bees quickly poisoned by the fumes. When dead they were easily shaken from the combs and the honey drained into large earthenware containers. The honey was allowed to settle in the container and any wax debris that floated to the surface was removed. This honey was called virgin honey. The remaining honeycombs were pressed to yield what was called common honey. The combs that remained after pressing were soaked in water and made into mead. Many beekeepers were unhappy at having to kill their bees. To reflect this feeling the following epitaph was found in an old German bee book:

> Here rests cut off from useful labour
> A colony of Industrious bees,
> Basely murdered by its
> Ungrateful and ignorant owner.

And the poet James Thomson (1834-1882) in his work *The Seasons* wrote:

> Ah! see where, robbed and murdered in that pit,
> Lies the still-heaving hive! at evening snatched,
> Beneath the cloud of guilt concealing night,
> And fix'd o'er sulphur, while not dreaming ill,
> The happy people, in their waxen cells,
> Sat tending public cares.
> Sudden, the dark, oppressive steam ascends, ...

STRANGE HIVES

By the early eighteenth century progressive beekeepers had devised more efficient methods for hiving bees than the simple straw skep. Thorley introduced simple box hives made of inch-thick deal in about 1730. These boxes were about 10″ deep and 14″ square. Bars were added across the top so that the bees could attach their combs. Windows were sometimes incorporated into a small beehouse that protected them from the weather. To complete the picture, red, white, blue, or yellow shapes in the form of half-moon, or square, were painted on the outside so as to distinguish one colony from another. No doubt these were delightful decorative features in one's garden but from a beekeeper's point-of-view they were rarely successful.

Around 1806 the Ukrainian Peter Prokopovich developed what must have been the first movable frame hive. The bars had grooves in them so as to permit the bees passage from one chamber to another. However, the bees still glued the frames to the hive walls with propolis and made them virtually impossible to remove.

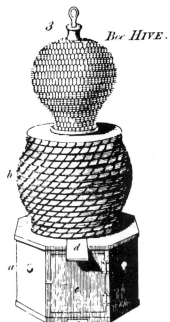

Box Hive.

GLASS BELL
JAR HIVE

In the mid-nineteenth century the practice of adding glass jars to the top of a hive was developed. The *Gardeners' Chronicle* of 16th August, 1856, reported that in a shop window in Trumpington Street, Cambridge, there was on exhibition a glass bell jar containing 96 pounds of pure virgin honey. The glass jar was hexagonal, about two-and-half feet in height, with a diameter of two feet.

Around this time Nutt invented a hive that incorporated a thermometer, in the belief that swarming could be predicted by watching for a small rise in hive temperature.

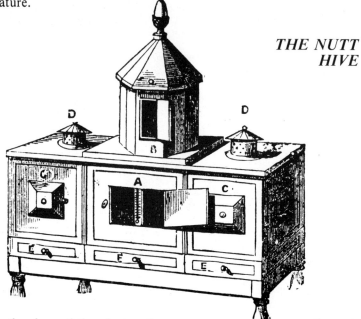

THE NUTT HIVE

Yet, by the close of the nineteenth century, so many supposedly perfect hives had been invented, that Hutchinson in his book *Advanced Beekeeping* (1911) quipped that any "beginner with a few brains, boards and a buzz-saw is the man of all others who feels called upon to invent a beehive."

BEST COLOUR FOR HIVES

The best colour for beehives has been found to be pale stone colour. However, it is best in an apiary to have hives painted with different and contrasting colours, this helps the bees to locate their correct hive.

THE FIRST OBSERVATION HIVES

The earliest observation hives were made in Roman times. Pliny tells us of a Roman Senator who had a hive made of the most transparent horn, this enabled him to observe the bees at work. Fixed comb hives that allowed the bee colony to be observed undisturbed began to be produced in the seventeenth century. Improvements were gradually introduced so that by the middle of the nineteenth century the observation hive, as we know it today, had been developed.

The blind beekeeper Francois Huber invented an observation hive that opened like the leaves of a book. The bees however could not survive in it during the winter.

PREPARING, OR DRESSING, A HIVE

For thousands of years hives have been "rubbed", or "dressed" with balm leaves as a preparation before taking a swarm. Pliny, the Elder (A.D. 23-79) mentioned this curious practice thus:

> Touching Balm which the Greeks call Melittus: if Beehives be rubbed all over and besmeared with the juice thereof, the bees will never go away; for there is not a flower whereof they are more desirous.....

Old British skeppists would use balm for "dressing" hives and this practice is referred to by Milton in *Paradise Lost* Book 1 (1.770) thus:

> As bees
> In spring-time, when the sun with Taurus rides,
> Pour forth their populous youth about the hive.
> In clusters; they among fresh dews and flowers
> Fly to and fro, or, on the smoothed plank,
> The suburb of their straw-built citadel,
> New rubbed with balm, expatiate and confer
> Their state affairs.

And Frank Cowan in his *Curious Facts in the History of Insects* (1865) tells of a related strange procedure for alluring a swarm:

> When a swarm is to be hived, instead of moistening the inside of the hive with honey, or sugar, the Bee-Master throws into it inverted about a pint of beans which he causes a sow to devour and immediately then it is said will the bees take to it.

A still more bizarre practice is described in Elspeth Huxley's book *The Mottled Lizard*. She describes how the Wakamba of East Africa "would rub a new beehive with mutton fat, put into it a certain kind of torpid lizard and enjoin the bees to be as peaceable as the sheep and the lizard. It was seldom however that the bees listened to this advice."

Furthermore the BBJ of July 1980 reported that in some parts of America beekeepers would rub broken peach leaves inside a hive so enabling it to hold a swarm from absconding. One beekeeper also had the habit of rubbing himself all over with peach leaves before taking a swarm — in this way he never needed to use any protective clothing.

NOVEL MEANS FOR PREVENTING SWARMING

The Apidictor

The Apidictor was a device patented by Mr. E. Woods, a BBC engineer. This electronic device gave an audible warning of an impending swarm at least 15 days beforehand. It sold for £45 and according to the *Times* of 16th February, 1960, was reported to be widely used in New Zealand, India and Germany. However, it never really caught on and its manufacture eventually ceased.

Wet cloths

An old method to stop swarming was to cover the skeps with cloths that had been soaked in cold water. The apiarists would soak them, using a watering can, two or three times a day. The sudden lowering of the temperature of the hive would subdue the bees and prevent a swarm emerging.

SETTLING A SWARM

Use of a mirror

It has long been known that the flash of light from a mirror directed at a swarm may induce it to settle. This technique has been used to prevent the bees clustering on high trees, or under the eaves of houses, where it would be difficult to hive them. The method has been described by Mrs. Bascom, of Oregon, in the *Scottish Beekeeper* of March 1974 thus:

> Starting in May I carry with me a 4″ mirror. When I find a swarm in flight I get into position where the sun will reflect the mirror. I pass the reflection in rainbow fashion just above the bees. As the bees get lower to the ground, I lower the reflection. They can be put almost anywhere by this method.

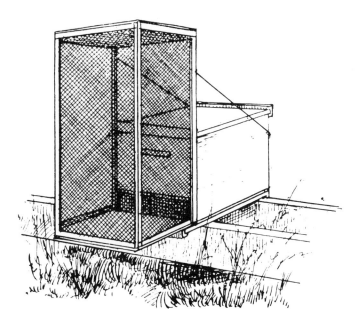

SWARM-CATCHER.

The Bee-Bob

Some apiarists suspend so-called bee-bobs around the apiary during the swarming season. These bee-bobs are small black velvet balls about the size of a fist, and were supposed to induce swarms to settle. One beekeeper the Rev. Thomas Hunt of Wyoming, Pa., developed this concept to ensure his swarms would not leave his apiary. At the beginning of the swarming season he would collect a number of dead bees and string them together using a needle and thread, so making them into a ball about the size of an egg. He would then suspend this bee-bob from a pole placed in a central position in his apiary. Invariably, so he claimed, this would secure every swarm.

STRANGE METHODS FOR SUBDUING BEES

The Hammer

Several beekeepers have informed me that in parts of Northern England, colonies of fierce bees are subjugated by means of a large hammer. This appliance is used to thump on the outside of the hive before it is opened. Apparently, bees that previously were vicious are subdued by this means.

The Puffball

The Rev. W. C. Cotton (born 1814) founded while a student at Oxford, the "Oxford Apiarian Society." This society published his pamphlet entitled: "A Short and Simple Letter to Cottagers." This was an attempt to save the lives of bees that might otherwise have been killed by sulphuring. To achieve this end, Cotton advocated the use of the puffball fungus to stupefy the bees when taking the honey harvest. He wrote:

> The fungus does them no harm; it makes them drunk,
> which is very good for bees, though bad for men, as they
> get well in 20 minutes and are all the merrier afterwards.

The BBJ of November 1942 informs us that the use of the puffball (Galvatia gigantia) was still in use in West Sussex and that beekeepers in the Godalming district occasionally employ smouldering Polyporus betulinus and Doedolea quercina to anaesthetize bee colonies. The same journal informed its readers in July 1949 that beekeepers on the Yorkshire Moors still use the puffball, however many of them are very secretive about it. In more recent times a firm in Timaru, New Zealand, is reported to use the puffball to anaesthetize bees during queen rearing.

In a study of anaesthesia of honeybees by smoke from puffballs, W. F. Woods reporting in the *J. Api. Res.,* (1983) p. 107, found that the smoke from burning human hair had a similar effect to that produced by the puffball. This he attributed to the presence of hydrogen sulphide in the smoke.

Laughing Gas

In the *Times* of 6th June, 1962 there is a report of how a colony of vicious bees, in an apiary in Schooleys Mountains, New Jersey, was subdued using laughing gas. The gas was found to render them docile and lethargic. It is interesting that some beekeepers place ammonium nitrate crystals in the smoker. This chemical on heating produces nitrous oxide (laughing gas), and so would explain how the crystals induce a colony to calm down. It has furthermore been discovered that bees subjected to this treatment always lose their memory with regards to their geographical location. Colonies so treated may be relocated to a new site without loss.

Chloroform

In the journal the *Naturalist* of 1858 (vol. 8, p. 189) there is an article entitled "Bee Taming." It describes how chloroform was used to collect a swarm. The following is an extract:

> On Wednesday a swarm of bees from a neighbouring
> apiary settled upon the window of a shop in one of the
> leading thoroughfares in Morpeth and by the attention
> which they excited threatened to cause some obstruction

to business in that part of the town. The master of the shop, however, who possessed some knowledge of bees, in the course of a very short time had the entire swarm rendered perfectly quiet and manageable by the application of chloroform. Having by this ingenious device been made completely harmless, they were carefully parcelled up and delivered to the owners.

The Glare of Torches

In the journal *Nature* for 1884, Mr. R. Morgan, Deputy Forester for Madras, gave an interesting account of how the fierce bees of this part of India were subdued by the natives: "they carry torches and knives to cut away the combs. The bees are roused by the glare of the torches but do not sting — although in daytime they are terribly pugnacious and many a traveller has barely escaped with his life after disturbing them."

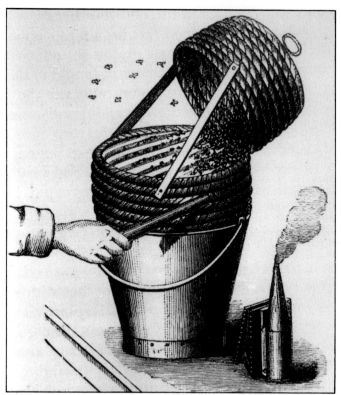

DRIVING BEES

Driving bees is the technique of forcing bees to migrate from a skep full of comb and honey into an empty one. This enabled the honey crop to be harvested without the need of sacrificing the bees, as would occur if they were sulphured. This old practice was accomplished by rhythmic beating on the sides of the skep. This seemed to have an hypnotic effect on the bees, inducing them to peacefully move upward to occupy the empty skep. It was an extremely skilled technique and during the last century there would be competitions at village fetes to see who could drive bee colonies in the shortest possible time.

The magazine *Punch* for 14th August, 1880 refers to the practice in the following way:

> How doth the little busy Bee,
> Increase her little power
> And gather favour every day,
> And almost every hour!
>
> How pleased she hears within her cell
> That Apiculture thrives!
> That honeycomb is selling well,
> **And Bees are having "drives."**!

The Strange case of Colonel Plant

Mr Edmund Hall, an accountant and beekeeper, of the small village of Oborne, near Sherborne in Dorset, one Monday afternoon in the year 1902, was called out to the farm of Mr. Ryall of North Wootton, in order to drive his bees. Having successfully accomplished the task he was sitting having tea with Mrs. Ryall, and his small son, who had accompanied him, when suddenly he got up from the table and cried out that he was going to faint. He immediately collapsed and died.

Subsequently it was discovered that the so-called "Mr. Hall" was in reality Colonel Edmund Plant of the 2nd Gloucester regiment, who was also the science master of Clifton College, Bristol. Colonel Plant had in fact resided in Bristol since 1861, and curiously his entry in *Who's Who,* had not mentioned his interest in beekeeping. His double life had been so successful that no one had suspected that the beekeeper and accountant Mr. Edmund Hall, who left for business each Monday morning, not returning till Friday evening, was in reality the science master of Clifton College.

THE POLITICAL STRENGTH OF THE BEE

In a recent report Greek beekeepers have threatened to disrupt the proceedings of the Athens parliament by throwing in hives of bees. Their irritation arises from proposed legislation following the entry of Greece into the EEC. Such demonstrations are not new. During the 1930's the Ministry of Agriculture in our own country proposed to introduce a "national mark" for use on all honey labels. Most beekeepers were violently opposed to this suggestion, which appeared to many to be unreasonable interference by the government. Many beekeepers got together and threatened to invade Whitehall with lorries carrying thousands of hives which they proposed to ditch in the centre of the capital. This threat caused chaos and panic. Newpapers carried the headline: "Threat by British Beekeepers...." As a consequence of the resulting commotion the Ministry backed down; so demonstrating the potential strength of the humble bee.

ARE BEEKEEPERS QUARRELSOME ?

Many people consider beekeepers to be a peculiar breed. Consider the view expressed in the *Times* of 6th September 1971:

> Nobody laughs at dairy farmers. Even pig breeding is considered a dignified occupation. But beekeeping — surely one of the most civilised of occupations — is usually reckoned to be good for a giggle. There is fair argument for saying that Sir Arthur Conan Doyle dispatched Sherlock Holmes to a beekeeping retirement in Sussex merely to heap derision on a character whom he hated.

It was the famous English apiarist W. Herrod-Hempsall who concluded that: "there is no occupation in which there are so many cranks as beekeeping."

In many ways beekeepers have brought this upon themselves. One only has to look through the past issues of any beekeeping journal to find time and time again beekeepers involved in trivial and trite argumentation. Even as far back as 1722 we read in Warder's book *The True Amazons* a bitter attack on a fellow beekeeper and author of *The English apiary*. This book, declared Warder, was "full of falsehoods and ridiculous directions" and its author, a Mr. Geddes, was "an ignoramous about bees".

Mr. Victor Dodd writing in the journal *Beecraft* for October 1979 declared that "Generally speaking.... time and time again one comes across the most bitter arguments (amongst beekeepers) on matters which are often little more than differences of opinion." Indeed, Dr. John Cumming, the *Times'* Bee Master, in his regular column devoted to beekeeping matters, would frequently create a response of surprising acrimony, generally over some very trivial matter.

One has only to look at the history of beekeeping in Britain to appreciate the truth of the remark that beekeepers are generally quarrelsome. If one looks back to the early part of the century when the British Beekeepers Association (B.B.K.A.) was a very much hobbyist and London based organisation, then the official journal was the *British Bee Journal* (B.B.J.). This journal was jointly owned by Cowan and Herrod-Hempsall. Over the years there developed a clash of personalities which culminated on one fateful afternoon in June 1943, when the B.B.J. withdrew its co-operation, and refused the use of its meeting room and library to the B.B.K.A. Furthermore the B.B.J. would no longer act as the official journal. Consequently, the B.B.K.A. was reorganised and the journal *Beecraft*, which had been founded in 1920, became the official voice of the British Beekeepers Association.

Throughout its history the B.B.K.A. has had a somewhat stormy history. The eminent chemist Walter Reid, president of the association in 1926, ended his links with it after the annual meeting terminated in uproar. This followed criticism of his conduct by others present. From that time until his death in 1931 he would have nothing whatever to do with the B.B.K.A.

One reader of the B.B.J. for June 1951, a Mr. K. Leng, had also gained the impression that beekeepers were generally very quarrelsome individuals. He wrote:

> As a reader of bee papers for the last few months. I am struck not only by the amount of disagreement on all subjects but by the fact that beekeepers appear much keener on trying to score off each other, and often in rather a nasty way at that, than on arriving at any particular truth. I had always imagined that these beveiled gentlemen, moving rather ponderously among their hives, were big hearted, patient and perhaps rather placid sons of nature. A course of bee paper reading has somewhat shaken that opinion.

AN IDIOSYNCRATIC BEEKEEPER

In July 1948, the Rev. E. N. Mellish, holder of the Victoria Cross, was ordered by the Ministry of Agriculture to destroy his bees as they had become infected with disease. He refused, on the grounds that he had a great affection for them. Accordingly he was taken to court. The court proceedings read today like something from a West End farce.

Conducting his own defence, the Rev. Mellish, argued that as the working life of a bee was only about three weeks, then the bees he had originally been ordered to destroy had already died. Furthermore, "I believe it is very unfair to ask me to destroy bees and I refuse to obey" he argued, adding that if he was ordered to kick a policeman he would also refuse to comply on the grounds that it was unfair to himself and the policeman.

At the conclusion of the trial he was fined one pound. He immediately responded to the judge: "What if I don't pay sir?" To which the magistrate replied: "please don't say that." adding, "If you could not pay you would have to show your means." To which the persistent defendant replied: "You can go to the bank today and you will find I have an overdraft." He then added that it might be better if he were sent to prision: "I have never been to prison yet, and I think it might be interesting."

ONE METHOD OF
TRANSPORTING
HIVES

BLIND BEEKEEPERS

Blindness has never been a deterent to beekeeping. One blind beekeeper, Mr. Charles Larson, commented in the *American Bee Journal* of August 1973, as follows:

> I cannot check bees alone but can detect several things without being told by sound and feel. I can detect a queenless colony, a hungry colony, one in need of supers, and when there is a honey flow.

The most famous blind beekeeper was Francois Huber, who was born in Geneva in 1750. This extraordinary man made many important discoveries in the natural history of the honey bee. As he was totally blind he depended upon the vision of his servant Francois Burnens. One ingenious contrivance invented by Huber was a hive consisting of frames that opened up like the pages of a book. This enabled every frame to be closely examined and the behaviour of the bees studied.

THE FIRST CHAIR OF BEEKEEPING

The B.B.K.A. held a grand exhibition of the Royal Horticultural Gardens, South Kensington, on 27th July 1880. The Earl of Spencer was so impressed that he proposed that a professorship in beekeeping be appointed to the Science Department of what is now Imperial College. *Punch,* celebrated this proposal with the following lines:

> How doth the little bee
> Increase her little power,
> And gather favour every day,
> And almost every hour!
>
> In Exhibition hive and tent
> She would be sharer too,
> So swarms to Kensington are sent
> Their busy work to do.
>
> And if Earl Spencer should reply,
> "The bees shall have a Chair,"
> To Kensington again she'll fly,
> And humbly settle there.

(Punch, 14 August 1880, p 71)

THE WORLD'S FIRST BEEKEEPERS CLUB

The world's first beekeepers club was founded in Glasgow at 104 Renfew Street in the dark days of February 1942. It commenced with a membership of eight, but by 1948 this had increased to more than 200. Beekeepers visiting Glasgow were welcome to drop in at the club for a friendly chat and cup of tea with fellow beekeepers. All were assured a hearty welcome. It was so successful that its members urged other beekeepers around the world to establish similar organisations.

2

BEES AND MANKIND

BEES AND WARFARE

Throughout history bees and warfare have had a curious relationship. Cowan in his *Curious Facts in the History of Insects* informs us that in parts of Hampshire there was a common belief that bees would be idle whenever there was a war. This certainly has been found to be untrue this century, as during both, the Great War and the Second World War, bees have played an important role and have definitely not been idle. In the First World War the Government of the day recognised the importance of beekeeping and enlisted in the national effort the services of many beekeepers. The Food Controller happened to be Lord Rhondda, himself a beekeeper of no mean reputation, having about 700 hives. Again in the last war the Ministry of Agriculture encouraged beekeeping recognising its importance not only in honey production but for plant pollination. Indeed, in the early stages of the war, when there was great fear that mustard gas would be employed against the civilian population, there appeared an article in the magazine *The War Illustrated* for December 1939, written by Major General Foulkes, describing how beehives could be protected from poison gas by charcoal-packed quilts.

However, bees have been employed in a more direct way in both ancient and modern warfare. In the Middle Ages both attacking and besieged forces used baskets of bees to inflict fear and panic among their adversaries. Even as late as 1902 beehives were used as weapons of war. This incident occurred in Brittany, when a party of peasants defending a Roman Catholic school used the hives as missiles against government troops.

However, the earliest account comes from English history, when around 908 A.D. during a siege of Chester, by invading Danes, the English under Ethelfleda, used beehives to repel them. The Danes, under Hingamund, attacked the city walls under hurdles, which gave protection from any rocks hurled against them. As a last resort the defenders dropped on them skeps full of bees, and the Danes were so severely stung that they abandoned the siege.

The next account comes from the continent, when in the year 940 the Duke of Lorraine laid siege to a stronghold of King Otto. According to a contemporary chronicle a large number of beehives were flung out against the Duke's horsemen. The bees attacked the horses so severely that the attack completely failed.

Sometime during the first crusade we find that the use of bees in warfare had spread to the East. The incident occurred during the siege of the Saracen stronghold of Marrah, some 50 miles from Antioch. In this instance the attacking Christians were repulsed when the Mohammedans fired beehives at them from their engines of war. Thus the earlier practice of simply dropping the hives had developed into something more sophisticated.

A similar use of military engines is described in a remarkable English illuminated manuscript now preserved at Christ Church, Oxford. This is believed to have been written around 1326. In the manuscript there is a picture of beehives, fully occupied with bees, being hurled at the enemy. However, the best account is to be found in the famous English poem *Richard Coeur de Lion,* written sometime in the thirteenth century. In this poem we read that Richard I, at the beginning of the Third Crusade had:-

> Two hundred shippes well victualled
> With force hawbecks, swords and knives,
> Thirteen shippes lade with hives of bees....

These hives were used to attack the enemy, as the poet continued:

> The Saracens them armed all
> And ran anon unto the wall;
> In white sheets they wrap themselves
> For the biting of his bees....

Eventually, the Saracens became more terrified so that they:

> Hid in a deep cellar
> That none of them might come near.
> They saw King Richard was full fell
> When his bees bit so well.

This poem indicates clearly that the beehive was now not simply a weapon of defence but one of attack.

We find another illustration in the fourteenth century poem *Godefroid de Bouillon.* This describes a siege of Acre sometime during the First Crusade, when 25 batteries began slinging beehives at the enemy. The bees attacked the Saracens in every possible way, making them flee the ramparts. The Sultan in despair called for his galley and fled the city. Thus it became known that the city of Acre had been "taken by bees".

In the early 1860's the Bee Master in the *Times* caused considerable commotion amongst beekeepers of the day by relating an instance of a Turkish ship ridding itself of an attacking privateer by hurling skeps full of bees at the pirates. Why his article caused as much commotion as the incident itself must have created is curious. Indeed the subsequent correspondence proved acrimonious to say the least.

In more recent times there has also been protracted correspondence on this subject in the pages of this same newspaper. It all followed a letter that was printed on 16th January, 1953. In it an account was given as to how the Germans, in the East African campaign of 1914-15, had frequently employed bees to delay the advancing columns of British troops. It would appear that trip wires had been placed across the narrow jungle tracks so that the British soldiers, clad only in shorts and shirts, would trip over a full hive of bees, causing considerable disruption. However, this account was disputed by a Mr. Covell who in a letter published on 23rd January, stated that the bees had not been deliberately employed by the Germans. He gave a personal account how during the battle of Tanga in November 1914 the British troops had been attacked by bees which, he believed, had been disturbed by machine gun fire. This view is confirmed by General von Lettow-Vorbeck, the German commander, who in his book *My Reminiscences in East Africa* told of several German machine gun positions put out of action by attacking bees. Mr. Covell went on to relate how troops on the march were occasionally attacked by bees:

> One such instance was during our march from Bagamoyo to Dar-es-Salaam when a bush fire was started by someone throwing a cigarette into the grass during a halt. This disturbed a nest of bees and some of the men were severely stung. I remember removing more than 50 stings from one man's head and neck.

THE GREATEST BEE-TAMER OF ALL TIME

The most remarkable beekeeper of all time was Mr. Daniel Wildman, who during the late eighteenth century kept bees on the roof of his house in Holborn, central London.

Wildman became noted for his remarkable control over bees which he frequently exhibited to the public. On several occasions he appeared before King George III with a swarm of bees hanging in festoons from his chin — being probably the first to adorn a beard of bees. Near the 'Three Hats' Inn, Islington, was a popular place for entertainment, known as 'Dobney's Tea Gardens'. It was here that Wildman exhibited his bees. A contemporary advertisement read as follows:

> **June 20, 1772.** Exhibition of bees on horseback! at the Jubilee Gardens, Islington (late Dobney's) this and every evening until further notice.

> The celebrated Daniel Wildman will exhibit new and amazing experiments never attempted by any man in this, or any other kingdom before. The rider standing upright on the saddle with the bridle in his mouth, and by firing a pistol, makes one part of the bees march over the table and the other swarm in the air and return to the hive again, with other performances too tedious to insert. The doors open at six, to begin at a quarter before seven. Admittance — 2s.

Mr Wildman frequently asserted that armed with his friendly bees he could face even the fiercest mastiffs. On one occasion while holding a swarm, three dogs were set upon him. The first mastiff approached him, whereupon Wildman detached a bee which immediately stung the dog on the nose, and the dog retired very much daunted. After this the second dog approached but was foiled as quickly as the first. The third dog having observed the fate of the other two swiftly retired with its tail between its legs.

COVERED WITH BEES

It has been known for swarms of bees to accidently settle on a person. Although unusual, this exceptional event need not have a fatal outcome, as illustrated by Shirley Hibberd in his book *Rustic Adornments* (1870) when he quoted from an old Scottish newpaper:

> The incident involved an elderly gentleman on whose face a swarm of bees alighted. With great presence of mind he lifted up his hat, hive-like, over his head, when the bees, by their natural instinct, at once recognising so convenient a home, betook themselves to his head gear, which he quietly conveyed to his garden.

In August 1967 Lady Plowden described in the *Times* a similar incident:

> Once a swarm landed on the head of a gardener I knew who was fortunately wearing a cap. Very slowly he moved to the doorway of an empty hive, lay down in front with his head low and the bees walked quietly into the hive.

Another correspondent, Mr. W. R. F. Spearman, related how while on holiday in Sumatra, a swarm of bees landed on his head and shoulders. His account continued:

> I stood still, not in anyway frightened as I did not know then the danger if a person panics. After about half-a-minute the swarm left me and I had not one sting. During this time the guide had fled for his life. Later he told me that this was uncommon and the natives were all terrified of the bees. He stressed that the only thing to do is to stand dead still and they probably wouldn't sting. Had I been aware of the danger I would have been terrified and fought off the bees with serious results.

Similar advice was also offered by Irene Lloyd also in the *Times* of August 1967. She wrote:

> I have heard of at least two reports when beekeepers came across a swarm in woodland but found themselves without any means of carrying it away. The procedure is to stand underneath the swarm, shake it over oneself and when settled to gingerly walk home. Arriving there the bees should be gently but firmly brushed off with a long feather. My general advice is to keep cool.

Record for a beard of bees.

The record for a beard of bees is held by James Johnson of West Virginia. His beard weighed 10 pounds and contained about 35,000 bees.

The technique for making a beard of bees is relatively simple. Firstly, the bees must be well fed so that they are unlikely to sting. The person must then be protected by pushing cotton wool in the nostrils and ears. The queen is then placed in a cage and held beneath the chin and the bees allowed to collect around her, so creating the appearance of a beard.

BEES USED TO PROTECT VALUABLES

From time immemorial bees have been used to protect valuables. In Kashmir, in India, there exists a particularly savage strain of *Apis dorsata,* which is the largest and most lethal of bees. Apparently colonies of this bee were frequently used by bandits to guard loot in mountain caves.

In the *Times* of January 1953 an account is given of how smugglers on the river Hamble in Hampshire would conceal their contraband under empty skeps in a local apiary. A little honey was all that was necessary to attract sufficient bees to deter any customs officer from taking a closer inspection.

Probably bees have been used to safeguard valuables in this way throughout history. One curious discovery described in the BBJ of February 1951 was the finding of the long-lost building plans of the Cologne Cathedral within a beehive. It is probable that they had been stored there during a period of uncertainty.

BEES AND PIETY

The bee since time immemorial has been a symbol of purity and piety. In William Laud's *Conference,* published in 1639, a hive of bees is used as the symbol for the Christian church thus:

> The Church of Christ upon Earth may be compared to
> a hive of bees, and that can be no where placed in this
> world but it will be in some danger. And men that care
> neither for the Hive, nor the Bees, have yet a great mind
> to the Honey.

The bee as a symbol of piety has led to many strange legends, one by Thomas Bozius is quoted in Charles Butler's *Feminine Monarchie* (the 1609 edition). It concerns a simple woman whose bees were inflicted with disease and consequently produced no honey. Following the advice received from another woman she placed within the hive some consecrated bread from the Eucharist. According to the legend, not only did it arrest the disease but that on opening up the hive to take the honey she found within: "a chapel built by the bees with an altar, the walls adorned by marvellous skill of architecture having windows conveniently set in their places: also a door and a steeple with bells."

Another legend, along similar lines occurs in the School of the Eucharist. This tells of a peasant who desired to get his neighbours' bees into his hives by attracting them with the Host. Indeed it worked, so the story goes, and all the bees of the neighbourhood were attracted to his hive, wherein they constructed a little church. However, when the unfortunate peasant approached the hive "the bees issued out furiously surrounding him on all sides, and so revenged the irreverence done to their Creator and so stung him so severely that they left him in a sad state. This punishment made this miserable wretch come to himself, who acknowledging his error, went to find out the parish priest to confess his fault to him."

These legends, no doubt, are derived from the fact that the early Christian church had strong connections with beekeeping. In particular beeswax was needed in the manufacture of candles. These would be made by dipping a wick, usually a pith of rush, into molten wax. One finds a curious background to the early use of beeswax candles by the early Christians. It would seem that as the first Christians were under constant persecution, their meetings were usually held in secret. In hiding places, such as the Catacombs of Rome, candles would have been essential for illumination. Eventually when this persecution ended the use of the beeswax candles assumed a symbolic role. However, during the Reformation the use of such symbols became unpopular, this dealt a severe blow to both the wax and beekeeping industry. Indeed whilst Luther and Zwingli were compassing the downfall of the Church of Rome they were also bringing hardship for the many people who were employed in the rural industry of beekeeping.

In early church literature there are many stories relating the involvement of bees with notable churchmen. In the *Lives of the Saints* we read that a thief once ventured to steal the bees belonging to Saint Medard, whereupon they:

> set upon the malefactor, and eagerly pursuing him which way soever he ran, and would not cease stinging him until they had made him go back again to their Master's house, and there falling prostrate at his feet, submissly to cry him mercy for the crime committed. Which being done, so soon as the Saint extended unto him the hand of benediction, the bees like obedient servants, did forthwith stay from persecuting him.

Saint Ambrose is frequently associated with bees as the patron saint of beekeeping. In fact Saint Benedict, to many, holds this position. Kennedy-Bell in his book *The Joys of Bee-Keeping* informs us that in parts of Brittany there were to be seen, at the time of his writing in the early 1930's, many beehives having a Saint Benedict medal suspended over the entrance.

All these stories and legends go some way to account for the interesting veneration usually given to bees by countyfolk. Bucke in his *On Nature* tells how in parts of Monmouthshire it was the custom to go to the hives on Christmas Eve at around midnight, in order to listen to the bees humming a carol of celebration of the nativity of Christ. Apparently this appears to have been a particularly widespread belief as this old German Carol indicates:

'Tis by our countryfolk averred,
And let no scoffer doubt their word,
That oft as Yule-tide wheeleth round,
The bees in hive by weather bound,
Hum only on this night for mirth,
In worship of our Saviour's birth.

A related legend is to be found in the *Magazine of Natural History* for 1829. This gives an account of an old man from Bedfordshire who held the belief, which was apparently common in that county, that singing psalms to his bees would make them more productive.

TALKING TO BEES

There are many strange customs that have come down to us from the distant past and involve the direct communication with one's bees. Even comparatively recently J. M. Dunning in his book *The Key to the Hive* written in 1945 tells of a local market-gardener in Bedfordshire who told his bees of his imminent departure to hospital he writes:

> On the morning of his removal to hospital he was taken round his garden in order that he might say "Goodbye" to his bees. There among the roses and raspberries this humble apiarist made his difficult journey touring his modest apiary. The hives were approached in something like affectionate ceremonial, while he tapped on each in turn and intimated his impending departure to the busy occupants.

"Telling the bees" of domestic happenings has a long and fascinating history. One tradition which has intrigued writers for centuries is that of informing the bees if a death occurred. The usual custom would be to "wake-up" the bees by rapping on the side of the hive and announcing to the occupants details of the bereavement.

In the BBJ of November 1891 we read of how this custom was performed in the Bradford area of Yorkshire. Apparently, following the death of a person, funeral invitations would be delivered not only to family and friends but also to the beehives, which would be served with identical invitations. It would seem that even in these late Victorian times it was firmly believed that if this custom were to be omitted then the bees would die before the year was out.

This tradition is not apparently confined to Britain, for we find in Benjamin Thorpe's *Northern Mythology* (1852), that similar customs existed in parts of Germany. And in John Brand's *Popular Antiquites of Great Britain* (1853, edition) an instance is given of a gentleman when at dinner, following the recent death of a relative, being surprised by a servant inquiring, whether his master would inform the bees of the event, or whether he himself should do so.

A writer in the BBJ September 1950 gave a possible explanation for this custom thus:

> In those days the beekeeper was a very important member of the community. It is inconceivable that the bees would be neglected on the death of the bee master. Rather it is more likely that the new bee master would be introduced to the bees with some ceremony and the death of the beekeeper announced.

Bucke, in his *On Nature* mentions that: "In some parts of Suffolk the peasants believe that when any member of their family dies, that unless the bees are put in mourning by placing a piece of black cloth, cotton or silk, on the top of the hives, that the bees will either die or fly away."

Jenyns in his *Book about Bees* tells of the Rev George Raynor apparently a well-known beekeeper in Victorian times, who once told an old countrywoman of his parish not to put her bees into mourning following the death of her husband. However, during the following winter the bees died and the reverend gentleman was never forgiven.

It is such instances that may have led to the belief that the bees of a deceased beekeeper might abscond on the day of the funeral. Francis Kilvert in his Diary mentions one such instance thus:

> *Thursday, 2nd June 1870*
> *I am told that Mrs Preece's bees all swarmed the day she died.*

Betsy Powner, in her letter to the *Daily Mail,* also records such an event:

> They say that when the owner of bees dies, unless they are told of the fact, they will all disappear. A remarkable thing happened to my grandmother many years ago. When she lay dying her bees left the hives, and coming through the open window of her room, settled upon the curtains of the four-poster bedstead on which she lay, and directly she passed away they all went back through the window, but not to the hive. They all disappeared.

One wonders whether they had been attracted by the smell of medicants used to treat the old woman, or incense if the lady had been given the last rites — or could it be the explanation is not so simple. Langstroth tried to seek such a logical explanation for similar beliefs that were held by country people in North America. He wrote: "Some superstitious folk in America assert that the bees sometimes take the loss of their master so much to heart as to alight upon a coffin whenever it is exposed." Langstroth further gave an instance of a clergyman who had witnessed a swarm of bees gathered around a coffin during a funeral, but some years later observed the same phenomenon around a freshly varnished table, and so concluded that it was the varnish rather than the deceased that the bees were interested in.

In other areas there were similar customs for marriages and christenings. On these occasions hives would be draped in red cloth. In the Cambrian *Quarterly Magazine* (vol. II, p. 215) we read:

> If there are bees kept at the house where a marriage feast is celebrated care is always taken to dress up their hives in red, which is done by placing upon them pieces of scarlet cloth, or one of some such bright colour, the belief being that the bees would foresake their dwellings if they were not made to participate in the rejoicing of their owners.

There have been similar strange customs accompanying funerals. Thomas Fosbroke in his *Encyclopaedia of Antiquities* (1825) outlines a custom of turning over the hives of a deceased beekeeper at the moment his coffin is taken from his house. Such an event is described in the *Argus* for 13 September 1780:

> "A superstitious custom prevails at every funeral in Devonshire, of turning round Bee-hives that belonged to the deceased, if he had any, and that at the moment the corpse is carried out of the house. At a funeral some time since, at Columpton, of a rich old farmer, a laughable circumstance of this sort occurred: for, just as the corpse was placed in the hearse, and the horse-men, to a large number, were drawn in order for the procession of the funeral, a person called out, 'Turn the Bees,' when a servant who had no knowledge of such a custom, instead of turning the hives about, lifted them up, and then laid them down on their sides. The Bees, thus hastily invaded, instantly attacked and fastened on the horses and their riders. It was in vain they galloped off, the Bees as precipitately followed, and left their stings as marks of indignation. A general confusion took place, attended with loss of hats, wigs, etc., and the corpse during the conflict was left unattended; nor was it till after a considerable time that the funeral attendants could be rallied, in order to proceed to the interment of their deceased friend."

BEES AS SYMBOLS OF FRUGALITY

Bees have always been employed to serve as symbols of thrift, and are frequently found on ancient coins. Even in modern times the skep has appeared on the currency of several nations including Britain. Thus Bank of England banknotes from 1838 onwards depicted Britannia alongside a skep of bees on her right hand side. This continued on £5 notes and over, until 1957. The skep itself continued on £1 notes until 1960, and the ten shilling note until 1961.

Thus the bee is the ideal symbol of thrift and frugality as the following story, which first appeared in Victorian times illustrated:

Many years ago a Bishop during his annual visit to his clergy was disturbed to find many living in great poverty. When in turn he reached the poorest parish, he anticipated that the curate there would be in the worst plight. However he was pleasantly surprised to find that this was not so. The bishop was amazed. "How is this," he asked, "you are the first pastor to have a cheerful face and signs of plenty in your house. Have you some private income?" The curate replied that he had and thereupon took the bishop into the garden and showed him his beehives. "There" said he "that is my income, my bank that never stops payment!" He then went on to explain that by selling the honey, mead and wax he so secured the affluence so apparent to the bishop.

BEES AND ELOQUENCE

The ancient Greeks believed that bees could be an omen of future eloquence. Pliny informs us that Pluto, as an infant, had been taken by his parents to Mount Hymettus, where they left him whilst they sacrificed to the Muses. On their return they discovered that a swarm of bees had settled on the child and had begun to make honeycomb in his mouth. This incident was taken to be a sign of the infant's future eloquence. In Butler's *Lives of the Saints,* a similar incident that occurred to the infant Saint Ambrose is recorded; today this saint is held by many to be the patron of beekeeping. In Robinson's *Archaelogia Graeca* (1827) we read that Pindar had as a youth been nourished by wild bees, and it was as a consequence of this he began to write poetry. Charles Butler, in his *Feminine Monarchie,* published in 1634, records that when Ludovicus Vives was sent to Cardinal Wolsey to Oxford, a swarm of bees welcomed him to his college by settling in the masonry above his study window. This was again taken as an omen of the wisdom of his eloquence.

BEE EATING

Bees have frequently been employed as an item of food. One traveller has recorded that the natives of Ceylon, when they came across a swarm of bees hanging from a tree would hold burning torches under them to make them drop. They were then collected and after boiling in water, proved to be an excellent food. Peter Martyr (1459-1525) writing of the Caribbean Islands described how the natives would "willingly eat the young bees roasted..." However the most famous bee-eater was the idiot boy of Selbourne who has been immortalised in Gilbert White's *Natural History of Selbourne,* thus:

We had in this village, more than twenty years ago (about 1765), an idiot boy, whom I well remember, who, from a child showed a strong propensity to Bees: they were his food, his amusement, his sole object; and as people of this cast have seldom more than one point in view, so this lad exerted all his faculties on this one pursuit. In the winter he dozed away his time, within his father's house, by the fireside, in a kind or torpid state, seldom

33

departing from the chimney corner; but in the summer he was all alert, and in quest of his game in the fields and on sunny banks. Honey-bees, Humble-bees, and Wasps were his prey, wherever he found them: he had no apprehensions from their stings, but would seize nudis manibus, and at once disarm them of their weapons, and search their bodies for the sake of their honey bags.....
He has been known to overturn hives for the sake of honey, of which he was passionately fond. Where metheglin was making, he would linger round the tubs and vessels, begging a draught of what he call Bee-wine. As he ran about he used to make a humming noise with his lips, resembling the buzzing of Bees.

Thomas Hughes, of Trinity College, Cambridge, has described similar scenes in a letter published in *Nature* in August 1881. He wrote:

I have known boys catch humble bees and eat honey in them; and probably many other animals have learned how to get at the sweet drop.

And along similar lines Oliver Goldsmith in his *Animated Nature* (1768) wrote:

As for honey, it is extracted from that part of the flower called the nectareum. From the mouth this delicious fluid passes into the gullet: and then into the first stomach, or honeybag, which when filled appears like an oblong bladder. Children, that live in country places, are well acquainted with this bladder: and destroy many bees to come at their store of honey.

BEES AND CHILDREN

It is well known that bees tend not to sting children even when given provocation. For this reason many children have been attracted to beekeeping and there are many famous child beekeepers. Sladen is probably the most renowned; he began beekeeping when he was just 13, and by the time he was 16, he had written a book on bees. Even more remarkable is the fact that he not only wrote the book, but he printed, bound and published it himself. Later an established publisher took it over and the commercial edition was issued in 1912.

One of the most interesting instances of child beekeepers was the Market Rasen School Beekeeping Company. This was set up by pupils of the Market Rasen Secondary Modern School in 1940. It was a properly established company, having an issue of 200 one shilling shares, which raised sufficient captial to purchase bees and hives. During this period in wartime Britain, when we stood alone against the forces of Nazi Germany, it was symbolic of the resilience of the British spirit. Accordingly, the endeavours of these children attracted the attention of the nation and for some years afterwards detailed reports of the progress of the company appeared annually in the pages of the *Times*.

BEES AS POSTAL MESSENGERS

The B.B.J. of 16 January 1902 informs us of one English beekeeper who used his bees to convey messages. He took the bees a long way from their hives and gummed to their wings tiny micro-photographed letters and then set them loose, whereupon they returned directly to their hives, so demonstrating that bees could be used in this way. The idea seems to have been taken up by the Japanese during the Second World War, when bees were employed to carry microscopic documents across enemy lines.

BEES AS FISHING BAIT

The *Sheffield Star* newspaper of 9 September 1948 reported that two boys had raided an apiary in search of bee grubs for use as fishing bait. The beekeeper involved complained to the Sheffield Juvenile Court that he had lost in all two hives of bees. The bench treated it as a serious offence and the two boys were dispatched to an approved school.

SAMSON AND THE HONEY BEES

In our Bible, we read in the *Book of Judges* (14 : 8-9) an account of how Samson discovered a swarm of bees and honey in the carcase of a lion. The passage reads:

> And after a time he returned to take her, and he turned aside to see the carcase of the lion: and behold, there was a swarm of bees and honey in the carcase of the lion. And he took thereof in his hands, and went on eating, and came to his father and mother, and he gave them, and they did eat: but he told not them that he had taken the honey out of the carcase of the lion.

Samson then gave the Philistines a riddle to solve within seven days:

> And he said unto them, Out of the eater came forth meat, and out of the strong came forth sweetness. And they could not in three days expound the riddle (v. 14)

However Delilah gave her countrymen the solution to the riddle. The account continues:

> And the men of the city said unto him on the seventh day before the sun went down. What is sweeter than honey? and what is stronger than a lion? And he said unto them, If ye had not plowed with my heifer, ye had not found out my riddle. (v. 18)

Many attempts have been made to discredit this account. For instance the Baron Osten-Sacken in 1893 published a pamphlet on this subject which was reviewed in the journal *Nature* of 12 April 1894. In this work the Baron put the following argument:

> The original cause of this delusion lies in the fact that a very common fly, scientifically called Eristalis tenax (popularly the drone fly), lays its eggs upon carcases of animals, and its larvae develop within the putrescent mass, and finally change into a swarm of flies which in their shape, hairy clothing, and colour, look exactly like bees, although they belong to the order Hymenoptera and have four wings, the female having a sting at the end of the body. The fly Eristalis belongs to the order Diptera, has only two wings and no sting.

The journal *Nature,* commented, that this "certainly appears to be the correct explanation." But is it? If Samson had only seen flies when he turned aside to look at the carcase of the lion, the riddle would have been pointless. Are we to believe he couldn't distinguish between a fly and a bee? And what about the honeycomb — this must have been real enough; the fact that he refrained from telling his parents that the honeycomb had come from a carcase is a reasonable course of action and only affirms the truth.

It is relevant to consider how long a time would be needed before the carcase of a lion would be cleaned and suitable for bees to occupy. It is certain that in this part of the world a carcase would be cleaned and dried within a few days, and what more suitable place to hang combs than from the arched ribs of a lion. As no time is specified between the killing of the lion and the carcase becoming occupied by the bees, there doesn't seem to be any problem here. Another view is put forward by the writer Oedman, he wrote:

> It is well known in these countries, at certain seasons of the year, that the heat will in twenty-four hours or so, completely dry up the moisture of dead animals and that without their undergoing decomposition their bodies remain like mummies, unaltered and entirely free from offensive odour.

Thus there are two reasonable explanations to support the account, furthermore there are many other accounts that have come down to us from the past which should suffice to remove any remaining doubt. In the writings of Herodotus we find the following passage:

> Now Amathusians, having cut off the head of Onesilus, because he had besieged them, took it to Amatheus and suspended it over the gates; and when the head had become hollow a swarm of bees entered it and filled it with honeycomb.

And a further similar instance is recorded by Napier in his *Excursions on the shores of the Mediterranean:*

> Among this pretty collection of natural curiosities (in the cemetery of Algesiras) one in particular attracted our attention; this was the contents of a small uncovered coffin in which lay a child, the cavity of the chest exposed and tenanted by an industrious colony of bees.

It would appear that people have been too ready to dismiss the biblical account. In my view the above explanations verify its correctness. Thus despite what many have said previously it would appear that Samson did know the difference between bees and blow flies.

3.

FOLKLORE

BEEKEEPING FOLKLORE AND SUPERSTITION

The B.B.J. of November 1891 reported that in parts of Northamptonshire it was supposed to be a certain omen of death if a bee entered a cottage. In Derbyshire and Lincolnshire it was generally held that if a swarm were to settle on a dead tree trunk within the garden then it was a sure sign of approaching death within the household. The same journal of August 1930 reported how a beekeeper once wrote to the newspaper stating that he knew that the superstition of bees landing on dead wood etc., was true, as a swarm had settled on a dead branch in his garden, and within a week his wife had died. The following week, he again wrote to the newspaper saying that he had received over a thousand applications for a swarm from that stock — all of them from unhappy husbands!

Another piece of folklore is that the first person to see a swarm will have ill fortune. This originated possibly by beekeepers themselves, in their attempt to discourage individuals to be on the look out for a stray swarm. A related belief is mentioned in H. J. Wadley's *The Behaviour of Bees* (1948), he mentions that good fortune is believed to be indicated if a swarm settles on a house. This does not appear to have been so for the Prime Minister, Clement Attlee, whose Chequers home was invaded by a swarm of bees in June 1950, as the following year he lost the election!

In the *Lincolnshire Chronicle and Leader,* of May 1950, there appeared an article on superstitions connected with swarms. Apparently in this part of the country it was commonly held that there was significance in the first swarm to land on a property that had recently changed ownership following the death of a previous owner. If the swarm were to be taken with ease then it was believed that the new owner would have a long and happy occupation. Another strange belief was that if a swarm were to be found in an open field then it was useless to hive it as it would prove unproductive.

In many parts of the country there was the old folklore that claimed bees would never thrive in the possession of a quarrelsome family; and stolen bees are never successful, but will always pine and eventually die. This is indeed an ancient belief for Pliny first mentions it thus:

> It is a common received opinion, that rue will grow the
> better if it be filched out of another man's garden; and
> it is as ordinary a saying that stolen bees will thrive worst.

With respect to the stealing of bees and hives an old Manx law of 1629 stated: "That the stealing and cutting of beehives in gardens shall be a felony in like manner to Death." This law was repealed, but not until 1817.

Folklore has it that it is unlucky to sell bees — except for gold. Hence during Victorian times the price of a swarm was frequently half-a-sovereign. This was no doubt a sensible piece of folklore designed to obtain a respectable price for one's bees. Nevertheless, many beekeepers would never sell their bees for money prefering to barter. In this way they believed they would avoid further misfortune. Furthermore some believed that it was unlucky to begin beekeeping by buying bees as one's first stock. Rather they should be either a swarm that arrived on its own, or else a gift. Cowan (1865) states on the other hand that: "bees must not be given away, but sold; otherwise neither the giver nor the taker will have luck." And he also informs us that in Western Pennsylvania it was thought by some of the old farmers that the vendor of the bees must be away from home when the hive is taken, otherwise the bees will not thrive.

There are numerous cases of bees attacking people who to all outward appearance have ill deserved it. According to folklore many of these individuals are not so innocent as they appear. Pliny solemnly cautioned against thieves and criminals approaching a beehive. This is repeated by Butler in his *Feminine Monarchie* thus:

> If thou wilt have favour of thy bees that they sting thee
> not, thou must not be unchaste or uncleanly: for impurity
> and sluttishness they utterly abhore....

PLATE 7

BEE'S SWARMING.

SWARMING ON A SUNDAY

It has been a common observation that swarms appear to be more frequent on a Sunday, than on any other day of the week. This is an observation of long standing for we read in Sir Walter Scott's *Rob Roy,* published in 1817, the following comment made by Andrew Fairservice, concerning bees:

> They are a contumacious generation, they hae sax days
> in the week to hive on, and yet it's a common observe
> that they will aye swarm on the Sabbath-day, and keep
> folk at home frae hearing the Word —.....

And in Shirley Hibberd's *Rustic Adornments,* published in 1870, we read: "We have had a great many swarms on Sundays just about the beginning of Church Time!"

The probable explanation of this phenomenon is that during early times the Sabbath was the only day of the week that most people had off work. It is therefore not surprising that the cottager observed more swarms on that day than any other. An alternative explanation is that the sound of the church bells calling people to worship somehow induced the bees to swarm. Indeed it is curious that, from the many reports, swarms do appear to be attracted to church towers, again one wonders whether it is the sound of the bells that induce them to settle, just as the old habit of tanging with a metal plate seemed to achieve.

BEE STING LORE

For most individuals a bee sting will be of little consequence, indeed it has been known for some beekeepers to suffer hundreds of stings without any serious after effects. Nevertheless the unpleasantness of the bee's sting is in sharp contrast to the desirable product of the hive namely the honey. This contrast has attracted fascination since time immemorial. Thus we have the proverbs: "Honey in mouth, sting in tail" and "Honey is not far from the sting", and so on.

Throughout the ages the greatest writers have written on this curious paradox of nature. Thus Ovid declared: "Deadly poisons are concealed under sweet honey." And Shakespeare wrote: "He is not worthy of the honeycomb that shuns the hive because the bees have stings."

Moralists, in particular have frequently employed this aspect of bee biology to enliven their writings. John Bunyan, for example, in his *Book for Boys and Girls* (1686) wrote one verse entitled *"Upon the Bee,"* it began:

> The bee goes out and honey doth bring;
> And some who seek that honey find a sting.

In earlier writings it was widely believed that bees could punish the promiscuous. Thus Pindararos in the fifth century B.C. wrote:

> Thou painful Bee, thou pretty creature,
> .... false Phoecus and impure,
> With sting has prickt his lewd villany.

OLD PROVERBS

An old English proverb which refers to the swarming of bees goes as follows:

> A swarm of bees in May,
> Is worth a load of hay;
> A swarm of bees in June,
> Is worth a silver spoon;
> A swarm of bees in July,
> Is not worth a fly.

The old Scottish proverb "to have a bee in one's bonnet" refers to anyone who is hair-brained. In Scotland it was also said of someone who is confused, or muddled, that his "head is in the bees."

4.

MEDICAL CURIOSITIES

MEDICINAL PROPERTIES OF BEES

Dr. Robert James (1705-76) wrote of the medicinal virtue of bees as follows:
Their salts are very volatile, and highly exalted; for this
reason, when dried, powdered and taken internally they
are diuretic and diaphoretic. If this powder is mixed in
unguents, with which the head is anointed, it is said to
cure Alopecia, and to contribute to the growth of hair
upon bald places.

And Frank Cowan quotes from another old writer on the same subject:

If bees, when dead, are dried to a powder, and given to
either man or beast, this medicine will often give
immediate ease in the most excruciating pain, and remove
a stoppage in the body when all other means have failed.

Galen crushed dead bees and mixed them with honey and wrote: "If you put
them on a bald head, you will see hair grow...."

Bee-tea is well known in the ancient literature of many countries. Dried
dead bees are mixed with hot water, which after cooling is sieved and made
into a refreshing drink. It is believed to have a powerful diuretic effect. It was
also used by the ancient Celtic peoples to treat hydrophobia.

Many of the ancient medical authorities relied on bees as a medicine.
Hippocrates, Galen and Pliny, all refer to the medicinal value of bees. Crushed
bees, for instance, when mixed with honey was used to treat toothache, dysentery
and carbuncles. And the ashes of burned bees was described by Pliny as an
excellent salve for all eye diseases.

THE CURATIVE PROPERTIES OF BEE BEER

Dr. W. T. Fernie in a paper read before the British Homoeopathic Society
in June 1891, described the remarkable curative power of so-called bee beer.
In this talk he told of how when a country doctor, in the area of the New Forest,
an old patient came under his care who was an agricultural labourer on the
local Squire's estate. The man became seriously ill and eventually took to his
bed and seemed doomed to sleep quickly in God's acre, with his rustic
forefathers. Although he received some treatment in the local hospital, he
nevertheless went from bad to worse and became at last so waterlogged as to
lie an enormous mass of shapeless humanity, semi-comatose, and babbling of
green fields, in a small attic at the top of the narrow, steep, cottage stairs.

It happened that on visiting him in this dire extremity that Dr. Fernie discovered in the garden, the man's wife and daughter, making a brew from waste honeycombs after the honey had been extracted. He suggested that they might give the sick man a portion to drink, and then left the place, being assured he wouldn't see his patient again.

About a week later on riding past the cottage, Dr Fernie wondered why he hadn't been asked for a death certificate for the old man. Curious, he dismounted and entered the house and to his surprise found on entering the living room, his patient sitting at table enjoying a hearty meal. His recovery, the patient assured Dr. Fernie, was due entirely to the bee beer.

BEE STINGS FOR RHEUMATISM

The tradition that bee venom has a therapeutic use entails a considerable history. A search for its origins is an almost impossible task but we may be certain that its roots go back to the early history of man. We find the first recorded observations from ancient Greek and Roman times. These observations were derived from the fact that the keepers of bees were generally able to maintain themselves free of rheumatic disease. In one of the earliest treatises of Hippocrates bee venom is extensively discussed. Hippocrates called it "Arcanum" and refered to it as a "very mysterious remedy". From this early date the use of bee venom in medicine has had a continuous history. We know, for instance, that Charlemagne, King of the Franks (742-814) was treated with bee stings.

September 17, 1909   DAILY MIRROR

VACCINATION BY BEES AS A CURE FOR RHEUMATISM

Thus for centuries the traditional belief in the virtues of bee stings was passed down from generation to generation. This has been particularly so amongst the peoples of Central Europe, for it was from this region that the use of bee venom re-emerged in modern times.

The first specific treatise on the medical use of bee venom appeared in 1858. In this year Dr. C. W. Wolff of Berlin published his book entitled: *Apis Mellifera : on the poison of the honey bee considered as a therapeutic agent.* Wolff is believed to have studied under a Dr. Herring. However the first detailed and systematic study was carried out by Dr. Phillip Terc of Marbury, Austria. He began using bee venom in the 1870's and continued with it over a period of twenty-five years. He is known to have treated more than 500 patients and applied over 39,000 stings.

There are innumerable recorded instances of cures arising from this treatment. I have collected a number of reliable accounts below:

In the 14 May 1904 issue of *Nature,* Dr. J. Newton Friend reported the following:

> A country schoolmaster in Norfolk, who suffered very seriously from rheumatism in the back, deliberately exposed his arms to the stings of bees and was stung all over his arms. By the time however that his arms were well again his rheumatism had completely disappeared.

And, Dr. W. T. Fernie in an article entitled "On the Medical uses of Bee Sting Poison" published in the *Monthly Homoepathic Review* of 1 July 1891, described how "his gardener, who also helped him in attending to his bees over several years and was often stung by them, had no attack of rheumatism during all that time, though he had frequently suffered from the malady before and had done so again since."

Dr. H. G. White writing in the *British Medical Journal* of 19 May 1934 related how an agricultural labourer came to see him as he was unable to grasp the handles of a wheelbarrow on account of his rheumatism. He recommended that he try the effects of bee stings. Accordingly, the man went to a local beekeeper and received half-a-dozen bee stings to each hand at weekly intervals over a three month period. After this time the patient was completely cured.

Finally, in the *Birmingham Mail* of 22 January 1948 there is reported the death, at 95, of Mr. George Bennet, who claimed to be Britain's oldest beekeeper. So agile was Mr. Bennet, that only a few months before his death he had been climbing trees to collect swarms. Apparently, Mr. Bennet claimed to have cured himself of rheumatism 25 years previously by letting his bees sting him. Throughout the remainder of his life he never suffered again from it.

5.

BEES AND THE ANIMAL KINGDOM

BEES AND BIRDS

An interesting letter published in the *Times* of June 1950 described the finding of a bird's nest inside a hive of bees. The bird was identified as a yellowhammer. Apparently, although it was a strong colony of bees, the bird had been undisturbed and had successfully hatched nine young. However, from subsequent correspondence, it would appear that the bird had been wrongly identified. As was pointed out, yellowhammers invariably nest near the ground and would be unlikely to have nine young. The bird was more likely to have been a great tit — a bird which frequently nests in beehives. Indeed the B.B.J. of 1902 reported that an Oxfordshire beekeeper had discovered in a strong stock of bees a tit's nest containing ten eggs. The nest had been built behind the division board and the birds had gained access through a defect in the roof. Frequently, however, the great tit will exterminate the colony of bees before it builds its nest.

There are many birds that prey upon the honeybee. I remember after catching my first swarm, I left it in a swarm box for a few minutes while I went in search of a hive. On my return I found the box surrounded by a group of persistent starlings, which followed the box around the garden wherever I moved it. Indeed it is well known that starlings are highly skilled in extracting the honey sac from a bee. An interesting observation was recorded in the *Entomologist* magazine for April 1898. It had been observed that following the introduction of the starling into New Zealand its habit of killing bees for their honey sacs was copied by the native parson-bird (or tui).

The best known bee predators are the bee-eater and the honey guide. The European bee-eater (Merops apiaster) is an infrequent visitor to Britain. However they have been known to breed as far north as Scotland. Dr. Eagle Clarke writing in the *Scottish Naturalist* of September 1920 described a breeding pair of bee-eaters on a sandbank in the River Esk.

The honey-guide (Indicator indicator) is an altogether strange bird. It is found in most of Africa, Borneo, Burma, and parts of South East Asia. its habit, from which it derives its name, is to lead men, or on occasions, the honey badger, to a wild honeybee's nest. It does this by flying above the man and making a characteristic call. Once the man, or animal, has located the bees' nest it will wait patiently for all the honeycombs to be removed and will then descend to take the scraps. According to African tribesmen if nothing is left for the bird, it will remember the individual and on the next occasion lead him, not to a nest of bees, but to that of a cobra, or other venomous reptile.

BEES AND MAMMALS

It is well known that bees have a particular dislike of horses and there are many recorded instances of bees attacking them. The B.B.J. of July 1896 recorded one such instance when a number of horses that were engaged in pulling farm machinery had been attacked and killed. The farmer, a Mr. Edwin Wide, found a way of deterring the bees, he wrote:

> Prior to the horses being taken into the field for work I made a solution of carbolic acid and water and with a cloth dipped it into the solution, then wrung it out after which I carefully wiped the horses all over. The result was that not a single bee stung either the horses employed.

Furthermore the strong aversion bees have towards horses is well illustrated in the following account of a Mr. M. Carey-Hobson, writing in the journal *Nature* of May 1883.

> A party of young men who had been springbok hunting all morning, off-saddled their horses during the hottest part of the day under the shadow of a great Krantz (cliff); they had just tied them to some trees when the poor animals were attacked in the most vicious manner by an immense swarm of rock bees from the Krantz, and so dreadfully were they stung that although the thongs that bound them were cut through as quickly as possible to enable the poor things to escape — one beautiful horse was nevertheless stung to death.

Similarly bees are adverse to camels. C. N. Buzzard in his book *Shining Hours* (1946) tells of an occasion when Professor Baldensperger, an expert apiarist, was on military service in Palestine, he and his brother accompanied a few arabs who were moving beehives on camels. One camel was stung and this caused all of them to stampede with the consequence that they threw off the hives and both the professor and his brother were seriously stung.

One mammal which is largely immune to the bee sting is the pig. Probably this is on account of its thick layer of fat that lies beneath its skin. The ancient writer Hollingshed wrote that in Poland it had been known for pigs to overturn the large bee-nests in that country and drown in the honey.

This has a ring of similarity to the curious story written by Charles Butler in his *Feminine Monarchie,* only in this instance it refers not to the pig but a bear; a paraphrase of the story is as follows:

> In Russia there are found in the woods and wildernesses great lakes of honey, which bees have forsaken in the hollows of trees. One day a peasant searching the woods for honey slipped down into a great hollow tree and sank in a lake of honey. For two days he was stuck and although he cried out for help, as it was such a lonely place his shouts were in vain. At length when he had given

up all hope of life he was saved by means of a great bear. The bear like himself was in search of honey and it climbed up into the tree and then began to let himself down backwards. The man now thinking his end was in sight grabbed hold of the rear of the bear and uttered such a yell that the bear being taken aback that it scrambled back up the tree, so pulling the peasant clear of the honey.

In Britain, the smaller relative of the bear, namely the badger, may be a problem for beekeepers. These animals are known to upset hives and steal the honeycomb, just like the North American bear. According to F. S. Stuarts's book *Beekeeping Practice,* if one fixes red cycle reflectors to the hives they will deter most badgers. Another enemy of bees is the humble hedgehog. This beast will consume bees, dead or alive, and may be frequently found on the alighting board of a hive making short work of the busy inhabitants.

BEES AND TOADS

The toad is another interesting predator of the honeybee, and is a most persistent one, as any beekeeper will vouch for. Indeed the toad is a very cheeky one and although normally nocturnal it will place itself directly outside the hive entrance, in the middle of the day, and not budge, even if one goes right up to it. A French beekeeper of the name, M. Brunet, described in the journal *La Nature,* of 1877, how on going into his garden, just before a storm, he found his bees crowding into their hives and in front of the best hive was a toad devouring the bees as they entered. M. Brunet, watched till twelve victims had been devoured and expected the toad's voracity would soon be punished with a sting, but in vain. Objecting to further loss, he seized the creature by one of its legs and carried it to a bed of cabbage, thirty yards or so, away. However, three days after this, on going out to the hives he found the same toad at its old work. M. Brunet let him swallow only two, or three, bees then carried him away fifty yards in another direction. Two days later the "wretch" was again found at his post, greedily devouring.

Frank Buckland, in his *Curiosities of Natural History* (1874) gave a similar account; he wrote:

> Toads are capital hands at eating bees, when they can get no other insects. A gentleman in Oxfordshire had a hive of bees in the cavity of a wall: a common toad which had taken up its residence in a hole close by was observed to place himself at the mouth of the hive, and to catch the bees in their coming from and returning to the hive, with much dexterity and activity. After witnessing the toad at work for some time and feeling convinced that, if his depredations were suffered he would eventually destroy the whole hive — the owner of the bees killed the robber and on inspecting his stomach found it full of dead bees!

BEES AND MOTHS

One of the most formidable enemies of the bee is the moth. These creatures enter the hive at night and deposit their eggs in crevices of the hive. The eggs hatch and the resulting larvae destroy the combs and ultimately may bring about the destruction of the whole.

In the January issue of *Nature Notes,* the Selborne Society's magazine for 1893, a Mr. J. R. S. Clifford, published some interesting observations on the death's head moth and its involvement with bees. Apparently, the previous July a friend had found one of these huge moths trying to gain access to a hive, having been drawn to that spot by the smell of the honey. On other occasions he had found one of these moths lying dead within the hive, and the bees being unable to eject so large an insect, had embalmed its body in propolis. And according to this writer, certain continental beekeepers have found that; "the bees are aware they are liable to the intrusions of this big moth and when in the old fashioned hives, the bees erect a kind of fortification at the portal. This is constructed with a narrow passage and a bend, past which the Death's Head moth is not able to pass and which its jaws are not able to bite through."

THE APIARY

6.
NATURAL CURIOSITIES

BEES AND ELECTRICITY

It is well known that the behaviour of bees is altered during thunderstorms and particularly by lightening. It has been discovered that bees returning to the hive during thundery weather are electrically charged and so may be rejected by their own colony.

Weak electric fields also tend to make bees aggressive. Even the electrostatic charges that may accumulate on the beekeeper who wears clothing made of synthetic fibre could influence the behaviour of a colony.

It is well established that bees hived near high voltage electric power lines produce less brood and are less productive. Furthermore, swarms that are hived near power lines frequently abscond or may turn vicious.

Scientific work has indicated how bees are influenced by weak electromagnetic fields. Thus bees when resited appear to construct comb having the same alignment to the earth's magnetic field as in the previous position. And, the famous waggle dance is also influenced by artificial magnetic fields.

Other studies have found that bees possess within their abdomen small amounts of magnetic material. However, to what extent bees use their sensitivity to magnetic and electric fields in their everyday life is still a mystery.

BEE STINGS — CURIOUS FACTS

The virulence of bee stings has been found to be influenced by environmental temperature. Thus stings received on a hot day are generally more powerful. Futhermore, the pollen eaten by the bee also affects the strength of the venom. Buckwheat pollen is believed to produce the most powerful venom.

In general, dark-haired individuals are less affected by bee stings than people of fair complexion. Women during menstruation are more prone to be stung and a women's period might be brought forward following a sting. And if a woman were to be pregnant, a miscarriage might result.

Alcohol on the breath will induce bees to attack and sting. However, alcoholics have an enhanced resistance to bee stings. Beck, in his book *Bee Venom Therepy* (1935) cited an instance of a 74 year old alcoholic beekeeper who was stung by more than 600 bees, yet recovered quite quickly from his ordeal. Alcohol in the blood is therefore thought to lessen the effects of bee venom.

With certain individuals bee venom may act like an addictive drug. Indeed Terc described one woman patient whom he could never satisfy her demand for bee stings, when these were applied for therapeutic reasons.

Rusden in his book *A Further Discovery of Bees* (1679) stated that bees "wont sting a dead thing". This is indeed true for bees have been used in a forensic context in order to ascertain whether an animal is alive, or not.

An emergency remedy for a bee sting to the throat, or mouth, is a teaspoonful of salt slightly moistened with water and slowly swallowed. The pain and swelling disappear very quickly. The B.B.J. for 2 October, 1902, reported that this simple remedy had saved numerous lives.

THE OLFACTORY SENSE OF BEES

Butler in his *Feminine Monarchie* (1623) informs us that bees have an excellent sense of smell and are able to recognize a stranger in the apiary. He wrote:

> In a word, thou must be chaste, cleanly, sweet, sober,
> quiet and familiar; so will they love thee and know thee
> from all others.

H. J. Wadely, in his book *The Behaviour of Bees* (1948) advises that the beekeeper "wash the smell of dog, and horse, of tomato and onion from his hands before touching the bees."

M. Carey-Hobson, of Cape Town, described in a letter to the journal *Nature* of 24 May 1883, how bees detest the smell of chopped carrots. he wrote:

> One of the Hottentot children upon our place playing
> near some hived wild bees, mischieveously chewed up a
> carrot and spat it into the entrance of the hive; the boy
> was perfectly naked and the next few minutes might have
> been his last had not the European gardener happened
> to be near and hearing his shrieks hastened to the spot,
> thrust the child into a newly dug trench and quickly
> covered him with earth; but he had a narrow escape for
> his life for he was literally covered with bee stings.

It is a very ancient superstition that bees by their acute sense of smell will quickly detect a promiscuous woman, and accordingly sting her. In a poem by Theocritus, a shepherd tells Venus to go away to Anchises and there be stung by bees, as a punishment for her misbehaviour. The poem reads:

> Go to Anchises now,
> Where hives and hollow trunks of trees
> With honey sweet abound,
> Where all the place with humming noise
> Of busie bees resound.

Furthermore, Pliny warns that a woman during menstruation should not venture near a bee hive, for; "Certain it is, that if a menstruous woman do no more but touch a bee hive, all the bees will be gone and never more come to it again."

HOW FAR DO BEES TRAVEL?

Shirley Hibberd in his book *Rustic Adornments* (1870) states that bees were observed on the Isle of May, at the entrance to the Firth of Forth, which is 4 miles from the mainland and that no hive was present on the island. The bees must have travelled that distance across open water. Another observer a Mr. H. L. Jones, reported in the B.B.J. of September 1933, that his bees would travel a distance of 5 miles.

HOW LONG MAY BEES BE CONFINED?

Mr. C. B. Gooderham, of Ottawa, confined his bees in a cellar during nine winters during the years 1920 to 1929. On average they were confined for 156 days, however he found that confinements lasting 175 days had no adverse consequences.

During the last century bees were transported by sailing ship to Australia; this meant confinements of about 80 days. Bees survived this ordeal only if they had adequate stores of honey and were given ample supplies of water.

THE LARGEST HONEYCOMBS

Apis dorsata is known to build masses of comb on the branches of trees, with no covering whatever. In "A collection of Papers on Beekeeping in India," published by Mr. Salween, deputy conservator of forests, in 1883, there is a description of some remarkable honeycombs, one being 7 feet long by 6 feet deep. This particular bee appears to be attracted to certain trees, the most favourite being the kanyin tree. On one occasion Mr. Salween counted no less than 39 combs in one nest, some of them being of prodigious size.

WHAT IS BEE BREAD?

Pollen brought to the hive is kneaded by bees with their mandibles and then swallowed. In time it is disgorged and then packed neatly into cells of the honeycomb. This substance is known as bee bread. An interesting observation regarding this substance was reported in the journal *Nature* of 30 September 1950. In this article it was described how mice that were fed on bee bread had less cancer than those mice fed fresh pollen. It was concluded that bees add to the pollen natural secretions that include growth inhibiting agents.

UNUSUAL LOCATIONS FOR SWARMS

It is curious that in general swarms settle in places that enable them to be easily collected, as Shirley Hibberd, in his *Rustic Adornments* (1870) pointed out:

Generally speaking, swarms alight in postions where it is the easiest matter in the world to deal with them properly and effectually.

However, occasionally swarms settle in strange and peculiar sites. It is also interesting that swarms during one season frequently pitch in the same place which in previous years had attracted a swarm, possibly due to the previous swarm leaving a pheromone at that spot. In the wild it is well known that swarms only select certain trees on which to settle.

One curious report found in the *Times* of 22 July 1950, related how a swarm had extinguished the Bourne Gap light buoy in Southampton Water. A message from the steamship Haslemere had reported that the light was out. When the harbourmaster had made the eight mile journey there by launch, it was discovered that all the bees had been killed by escaping gas from the buoy.

In the same newspaper of 11 July 1951 it was reported that the clock in the tower of St. Nicholas's Church Bromham, Wiltshire had been suddenly stopped by a swarm of bees. Apparently they had settled in its mechanism and begun building comb. W. Herrod-Hempsall in his book *Beekeeping New and Old,* informs us that a swarm once settled inside the bronze model of a cockerel on a monument in Brest, in France. Another report describes how a swarm took up residence in the mouth of a large terra-cotta lion situated over the entrance of a brewery at Princess Risborough. Canning Williams mentions a number of interesting locations of swarms, including: a top-hat in an old wardrobe; a church organ pipe; a rat hole in the ground; a school clock, and in part of a Big Bertha, the First World War supercannon.

Some Interesting Locations of Swarms

Date	Place	Reference
July 1813	inside a lady's parasol	*Observer*, 25 July 1813
July 1950	on the Bourne Gap light	*Times*, 22 July 1950
July 1951	church clock at Bromham, Wilts	*Times*, 11 July 1951
June 1952	tower of Worcester Cathedral	*Times*, 15 June 1953
June 1964	church clock at Peckham	*Times*, 8 June 1964
July 1966	High Street, Tunbridge Wells	*Times*, 11 July 1966
1966	Wing of RAF aircraft	*Beecraft*, December 1981
July 1972	inside a pottery kiln	*Brit. Clay Worker*, Oct. 1972

* * *

QUELLING BEES BY THROWING DUST

Angry bees may be readily quelled by throwing into the air handfuls of sand, or dust. this was a fact familiar to Virgil, for he wrote: "A little shower of dust will quickly quell, These ardent passions....."

In Africa bees so dislike dust storms that the natives quell swarms of vicious bees by throwing up large handfuls of sand. The bees believe that this is a sand storm and immediately settle. Some beekeepers in Britain have also found this a useful trick whereby they can make a swarm settle.

The same method may be used to stop an attack by vicious bees as is illustrated in the following account by Dr. de Castro, and published in the *Indian Med. Gaz.* of 1927:

> One afternoon in January 1919 a party of us were in butts scattered along a wide strip of sand awaiting the return of demoiselle cranes from the fields. No one had informed us that there was a huge beehive under the bridge and Mr. K. of the police had his butt not more than 30 yards from this place. As the cranes came sailing past a regular feu de joie started, but very soon gave place to the most awful yells from K. He was soon racing across the strip of sand to the river with a thick swarm of bees about him. Seeing his plight, one of the party to divert the attention of the bees fired a charge of small shot into them and at the same time got his gun boy to throw up as much sand as possible into the air. I do not know the virtue of this procedure but it certainly had the desired effect for almost immediately the bees all left him and flew back to the hive.

BEES AND YELLOW RAIN

During the late 1970's claims were made by the U.S. State Department that toxic chemicals had been used during warfare in Laos and Kampuchea. Reports suggested that many people had died and many others had been injured, by yellow material sprayed from aircraft. This became known as yellow rain, on account of the appearance of yellow spots on the leaves of plants.

However examination of the yellow spots collected during 1981-82, at sites supposedly subjected to chemical weapon attack revealed surprising findings. Firstly, most of the samples contained a high proportion of pollen. Secondly, comparison of the pollen with that found in the faeces of bees revealed many similarities, so much so, that it was concluded that yellow rain was simply bee excreta. Furthermore it was concluded that it resulted from defaecation flights of massive colonies of wild bees.

Yet, despite these findings some investigators have suggested that the presence of pollen in the samples was so bizarre that they had to be fakes and must have been painted on the leaves. Thus the mystery of yellow rain remains unsolved.

CAN BEES HEAR?

Whether, or not, bees can hear is still a matter of debate. At one time it was thought that bees could only hear sounds that set up vibrations in solid surfaces, which were then detected by receptors on the bee's legs. However, recent studies have found that there are several rows of hairs situated behind the eyes which are capable of responding to sound waves. Thus when a swarm is thrown down upon the floor board the queen sends out specific calls that enable the bees to locate her.

The so-called "queen-piping" refers to the sounds heard just before a swarm comes off. This has been known for many years. Two types of sound have been recognized: "quacking" the sound emitted by a young queen still confined to her cell; and "tooting" the sound given by a young queen after she is free on the combs. The mechanisms by which the bees generate these sounds remain a mystery.

BEES COLLECTING FROM STRANGE LOCATIONS

Alfred Neighbour in his book *The Apiary* (1866) states that bees will collect sugar from any source. To illustrate the point he related how an old woman who kept a sweet shop in an adjacent street to where he had an apiary, used to receive frequent visits from his bees. At first the old dame found their visits interesting, but he continued:

> If the few pioneers who had the sagacity to find such a store had kept the secret only to themselves, their company would not have been objected to. Such selfish policy does not however accord with the social instinct of bees, and these soon informed their companions of

their good fortune. Day by day the swarms of these uninvited visitors increased, until all legitimate customers were beaten off; and the old dame found her stock of goodies diminishing by the thefts of these brigands of the air.

In the B.B.J. for 19 August 1950 there is a report of how work at a lime juice factory was disrupted by an invasion of bees. And at a jam factory the position became so difficult that work had to be suspended during daylight hours on account of swarms of bees. This journal also recalled how Mr. Canning Williams, of Southend-on-sea had once discovered pink honey in his hives. For a time he was baffled, until he was informed that his bees had been collecting from a local rock factory! The same journal, of January 1902, reported that bees were found collecting sawdust from a sawmill and taking it back to their hives. It was concluded by the writer that it was probably sawdust of a conifer tree, and that the bees were collecting it on account of its resin content, in order to make propolis.

In the literature there are frequent references to bees collecting soot. One writer in the B.B.J. of January 1902 described how he had: "frequently seen bees three, or four, at a time about the tops of our chimney pots.... these bees were seen to be dusty with soot." And another correspondent wrote: "for some weeks my bees have been collecting soot! Hundreds of them flew out of the stove flue in my study. They were quite black with soot and most were carrying loads of soot back to the hive."

Some writers have concluded that the bees in these instances were not actually collecting soot, but were simply prospecting in chimneys for a suitable place to swarm, and in so doing became smeared with soot. Chimneys, are indeed attractive to bees, and there are many reports of swarms settling in such. For instance, in the *Times,* of 16 July 1976, there is a report of how the Croft Nursing Home, at Kidderminster, was forced to close down on account of a swarm of bees which had taken up residence in the main chimney.

Observatory Bee-house.

BEES AND THE WEATHER

In many ways the behaviour of bees is governed by the weather. We find that many empirical observations which have come down to us from the past, have now been confirmed from scientific study. For instance, it is generally accepted today that bees can warn of a coming storm. Virgil was familiar with this notion, for he wrote:

> Nor dare they stay,
> When rain is promised, or stormy day:
> But near the city walls their watering take,
> Nor forage far, but short excursions make.

And, Willsford in his *Nature's Secrets,* writes: "Bees in fair weather, not wandering far from their hives, presage the approach of some stormy weather...." Tickner Edwards in his book, *Life of the Honey Bee* (1908) also writes: "in certain states of the weather — when thunder is about, and the air is tense and still — bees will often sheath their barbed daggers in any human skin, even that of their owner."

Herr Emmerig of Lauingen, in Germany, wrote in the journal *Die Natur,* of 1885, that from his careful observations, bees may indeed act as storm warners. He found that on the approach of thunder, bees that otherwise would be gentle and harmless, became excited and would attack anyone, even their usual attendant. He furthermore gave a succession of instances when he had found both the barometer and hygrometer predicting a storm, but his bees remained quiet — and no storm occurred — and vice versa. Emmerig concluded that bees were exceptionally accurate indicators of impending storms.

57

7.

CURIOUS FACTS ON HONEY

THE MYSTERY OF THE GREEN HONEY

In the late 1960's the Ministry of Agriculture made available denatured sugar to beekeepers at a reduced cost. It was ordinary table sugar to which had been added a harmless green dye. This was to ensure that the sugar was only used for feeding bees. In the B.B.J. for August 1969 there is an advertisement for this sugar which "could be delivered in ton quantities" from the company Edward Billington and Sons, of the Cunard Buildings, Liverpool. Soon beekeepers were amazed to discover that the honey when harvested appeared blue-green. This at first aroused considerable speculation and led to a protracted correspondence on the subject within the pages of the *Times,* for most of February 1971. Eventually the realization dawned that it was as a consequence of over-feeding with the denatured sugar.

STRANGE USES FOR HONEY

As it was well known that honey would prevent putrefaction it was an ancient practice for the dead to be immersed in honey. This was certainly carried out from an early period by the Assyrians. And the body of Agesipolis, King of Sparta, who died in Macedonia, was sent home in honey, as were also the bodies of Agesilaus and Aristobulus. According to many accounts the body of Alexander the Great was deposited in honey. Also the body of Justin II was placed in honey and mixed with spices. The wish of Democritus to be buried in honey is likewise confirmation of this widespread practice.

During ancient times honey was also employed to preserve fresh fruit. Furthermore, Pliny informs us that certain worms useful in medicine, were preserved fresh in honey. And in order to preserve the famous purple dye of antiquity, honey would be poured over it. Plutarch in his *Life of Alexander,* relates how Alexander discovered in the treasury of Susa, 500 talents of the purple dye, which was in perfect condition, yet was at least 200 years old. Its preservation being due to a covering of honey.

TAKING A BATH OF HONEY

John Gutch in an article in *St. Bartholomew's Hospital Journal* of February 1897 describes a curious remedy, that of taking a bath in honey. The writer states that such a strange treatment is admirable for aches and "strong itches." he quotes as follows:

> A friend of his had such a foul itch that he was like a leper, yet was cured by this treatment. He took an empty wine cask, called a pipe, and took out one head, and made a liquor of water and honey, making it pretty strong

with the honey and heating it as hot as he could endure
to stand in it, and put it in the pipe and caused him to
stand in it up to his neck, and this he did three days, one
after another, and he was recovered as clear as ever.

HONEY AND BUTTER

From antiquity honey mixed with butter has been a food for children. Thus
we read in the book of *Isaiah* (7, v.14-15):

Behold, a virgin shall conceive, and bear a son, and
shall call his name Immanuel.
Butter and honey shall he eat......

In India there is a tradition that a mixture of honey and clarified butter be given
as a respectful offering to a guest, or a bridegroom. And in one Hindu ceremony
honey is placed in the mouth of a new born infant.

D'Arvieux during his travels in Arabia in the nineteenth century found that
honey and butter mixture was still eaten by the Arabs, he wrote:

One of their chief breakfasts is cream or, fresh butter
mixed with honey; these do not seem to suit very well
together; but experience teaches that this is no bad
mixture nor disageeable in its taste if one is ever so little
accustomed to it.

And more recently, Captain Irby and Mangles, in their book *Travels in Egypt,*
speaks of the same custom:

They gave us honey and butter together with bread to
dip in it; Narsah desiring one of the men to mix it for
us. The Arab stirred it with his fingers, showed his
dexterity at consuming as well as mixing.

HONEY AND LONGEVITY

Pythagoras, who maintained a diet involving a great deal of honey, lived to the age of ninety. One of his disciples, Appolonius, lived on ambrosia — a mixture of milk and honey — and lived to be 113 years old. Hippocrates also prescribed a daily dose of honey for those who wished to live a long life. And the Essenes, a monastic Jewish sect, at the time of our Lord, were believed to have been beekeepers, and all lived to great age. Pliny, the Elder, wrote more about honey than any other ancient writer. In his *Natural History,* he records that there were 124 centenarians living in the region between the Apennine mountains and the River Po. This area was populated by many beekeepers.

Honey appears to have been an important part of the diet of the ancient Britons. The original bardic name for Britain, actually meant "The Isle of Honey." Beekeeping, in these early times was a major industry, and honey was the principal commodity. When Pliny visited Britain he commented that, "These islanders consume great quantities of honey brew." And Plutarch observed that "These Britons only begin to grow old at 120 years of age."

HONEY AND MARRIAGE

Every marriage contract in ancient Egypt required the bridegroom to promise to supply his bride with honey throughout their marriage. In parts of Asia it was held that honey could affect the fertility of women. And in early Hindu marriage ceremonies, in India, honey was served to each of the guests; during the ceremony the bride would be anointed on her forehead, lips, eyelids and ear lobes with honey. It was believed that the great purity of honey would ensure that the couple would have many years of happiness ahead.

There are a number of possible origins of the word "honeymoon." In Morocco, honey was eaten during a wedding ceremony and the bridegroom was expected to feast on honey in the days following the marriage. Another possible origin comes from the custom of the Teutones — a people who lived in northern Europe, they would drink mead, made of honey, for a period of thirty days after a marriage, hence — "honeymoon."

POISONOUS HONEY

Poisonous honey has been known to exist since antiquity. There are references in the Old Testament suggesting that some honeys may have unpleasant side reactions, thus: "Hast thou found honey? eat so much as is sufficient for thee, lest thou be filled therefore and vomit it." *Proverbs* ch. 27, v. 16) The most famous account of toxic honey is that given by Xenophon in the fourth book of the *Anabasis*. In 400 B.C. Xenophon's army of ten thousand men had reached the area on the Black Sea near Trebizond. The account continues:

> The number of beehives was extraordinary and all the soldiers who ate of the combs lost their senses, vomited and were affected with purging, and none of them were able to stand upright. Those who had eaten only a little behaved as if drunk, and those who had eaten much were like madmen. Others were like persons on the point of death. Consequently they lay on the ground in great numbers as if it had been a defeat. The following day not one of them was found dead, and they recovered their senses about the same hour that they had lost them on the day before. On the third and fourth day they were able to get up and felt as if they had taken medicine.

This account quite clearly points out that the troublesome honey was not wild honey, but honey actually taken from beehives. One may presume that the local people would have later consumed this honey so why was it toxic to Xenophon's men? Probably the explanation is that they had eaten unripe honey in which toxins were present. If the honey had been allowed to mature these toxins would have disappeared.

We know today that in parts of Georgia and Florida honey from the yellow jessamine (Gelsemium sempervirens) is poisonous only when it is uncapped. An incident was described by F. C. Pellett in 1885 when three children died from eating this honey when it was unripe. Whereas eating the ripe honey was perfectly safe.

Other honeys obtained near Trebizond are also known to be toxic. The honey of Heracleia Pontica further to the west was occasionally known to make those who had eaten it roll on the ground in considerable pain. Colchis, further to the north also produced a toxic honey known as "maddening honey." Strabo (60 B.C. —20 A.D.) the Greek geographer recorded that Colchian honey was bitter. In more recent times the traveller Evliya Effendi warned people against eating this honey. He also advised against eating honey of the Erzerum province, thus:

... bread and honey are rather to be suspected, for I
myself, poor Evliya, having eaten some honey in the
commander's house, became in half-an-hour so giddy
that I thought of throwing myself down from the castle.
(von Hammer, *The Travels of Evliya Effendi* II, p. 119)

The French botanist Joseph ·Tournefort (1656-1708) attributed the
poisonous honey to two species of rhododendron after local people had informed
him that the perfume of the flowers caused severe headaches.

The honey from the Trebizond area is probably the most famous but other
poisonous honeys are known. In North America during the autumn of 1790
extensive mortality occurred amonst those who had eaten honey in the
neighbourhood of Philadelphia. The American government became so concerned
that an inquiry was set up to investigate the incident. This concluded that the
honey had been obtained from the mountain laurel (Kalmia latifolia). In more
recent years this plant has caused similar problems, indeed it has been known
for beekeepers to throw hundreds of pounds of honey into rivers and streams
if they think their bees have collected nectar from this plant. Futhermore in
certain parts of Western North Carolina it is impossible to produce edible honey
because of the presence of this plant.

Some people have treated the whole problem of poisonous honey with
disbelief. One reason being is that it is very difficult to get the same reaction
to the honey in different seasons. (This problem has been apparent since
antiquity as Pliny was considerably puzzled by it). A further difficulty has been
identifying the toxic constituent of the honey. For example, a sample of the
toxic honey from North Carolina was found to be pure by analysts in
Washington, however the County Apiarist after eating a small sample wrote:
"there was a tingling of the fingers and toes as if the circulation had been
stopped. Very soon it was difficult to stand. This was followed by a severe
headache which lasted a couple of hours."

According to the Russian writer Z. Gutnikova, poisonous honey is obtained
from the leather-leaf plant. This honey is slightly yellow in colour with a
somewhat bitter taste and granulates readily. Apparently it is toxic to man but
not for bees. When small amounts are eaten, it produces violent headaches,
shivering, nausea and vomiting. As little as one teaspoon is sufficient to lead
to delirium and loss of consciousness. In the Khabarovsk region of Russia so-
called "heady honey" is obtained from the marsh tea plant.

Lord Macaulay (1800-1859) in his essay on Milton refers to the melancholy
of Dante as: "resembling that noxious Sardinian soil of which the intense
bitterness is said to have been perceptible even in its honey."

Macaulay was wrong in his assumption that it was the bitterness of the soil,
for we now know it to be due to the bees collecting nectar from a local variety
of wild parsley. Recent investigations have shown the toxin in this honey to
be a new type of alkaloid.

In South Africa the missionary Robert Moffat (1795-1883) described coming
across a plant of the Euphorbia family which produced a poisonous honey.
When eaten the honey gave a burning sensation in the throat; and in the Pretoria
region it was known as "Noors honey."

APPENDIX

BEEKEEPING FACTS AND FIGURES

Number of beekeepers in England and Wales

Year	Number
1946	83,444
1948	87,078
1950	91,729
1956	56,925
1966	39,122
1970	29,825
1979	31,000
1980	34,762
1985	36,443
1987	33,300

---
*

The cost of bees

1894	Swarm (4 lb) £ 0.40
1903	Stock (6 combs) £ 1.50
1979	Stock (6 combs) £49.50
1988	Stock (6 combs) £59.50

---
*

The price of English honey

Year	price per pound
1530	1p
1911	3p
1973	57p
1980	185p
1988	195p

THE EARLIEST SWARMS

Date	Place	Report
Date	*Place*	*Report*
23 March 1896	Essex	*Nature,* 2 April 1896
13 April 1972	Herts	B.B.J. 1972 p. 119
15 April 1943	Essex	B.B.J. 1950 p. 303

———————————————— * ————————————————

THE LATEST SWARM

Date	Place	Report
Date	*Place*	*Report*
27 December 1894	Spalding, Lincs.	*Nature,* 1895, p. 230

RECORD HONEY YIELD FROM A SINGLE HIVE

Yield lbs	Beekeeper	Year	Location	Reference
839	A. E. Schnetzer	1945	South Africa	BBJ, 1982 p. 154
486	N. Knight	1940	Suffolk	BBJ, 1980 p. 90
439	Mr. Noyes	1916	Minehead	BBJ, 1980, p. 90
412	L. A. Squires	1929	West Mercia	BBJ, vol 64, p. 66
383	J. Berry	1921	Llanrwst N.Wales	BBJ, vol 50, p. 48
352	L. Quayle	1899	Isle of Man	BBJ, vol 27, p 412